*Think of those
who dug the stone
and made the chippings,
slabs and sets,
for all those roads
and pathways,
trodden on.*

Published in 2018 by
Saddletank Books

Printed and bound
in Wales

ISBN 978-0-9927239-8-9

Isabel
The Little Staffy Engine

Written & illustrated by
Pauline Hazelwood

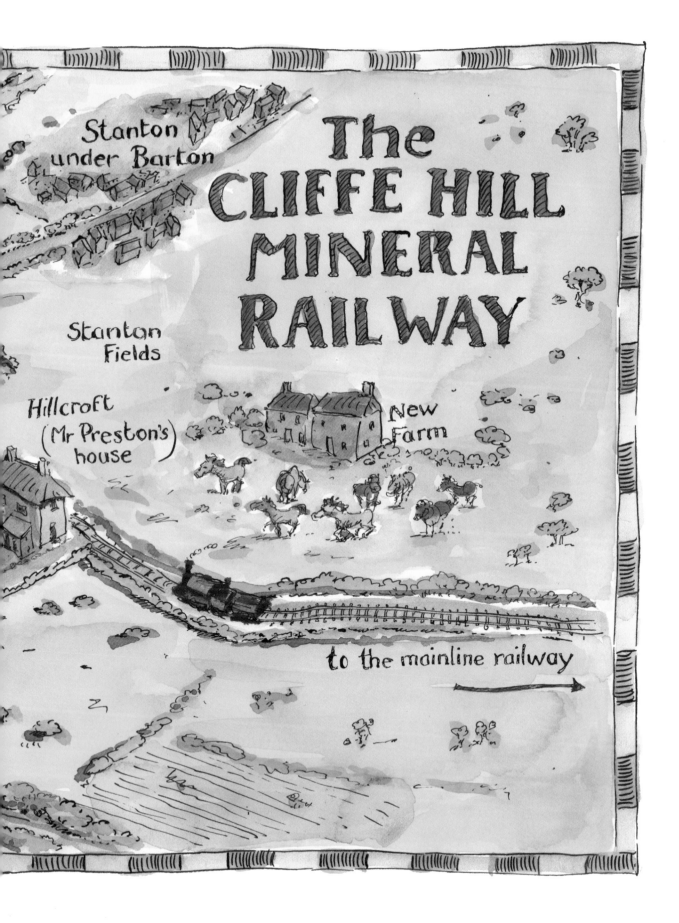

Stanton under Barton

The CLIFFE HILL MINERAL RAILWAY

Stanton Fields

Hillcroft
(Mr Preston's house)

New Farm

to the mainline railway

In the quarry, men dug out hard granite rock for cobbled streets, and the smaller stones were washed and pulverised in jaw crushers for dusty roads.
Horses and traction engines pulled the wagons of stone, and every day, children would bring lunch to the quarry for their fathers.

"I think a steam engine would do this work nicely," said Mr. Preston, the quarry manager, "but I haven't got much money!"

"Aha!" said Mr. Bagnall, who made engines. "I can make one for you, with no cab, a short chimney and a cheap round firebox."

"Indeed." said Mr. Preston.

"And you don't have to pay me all at once." said Mr. B.

"Excellent," said Mr. Preston, "I'll take two!"

The engines arrived,
and Isabel, Mr. Preston's daughter, loved them.
So much so, that he said, "We must name one after the
quarry, and one after
you!"

A rail track was set down, and Isabel chuffed off to work with Cliffe.

For a whole year, Isabel, the engine, hauled granite around the lumpy bumpy quarry, up the steep slopes and all along the tramline. "My frames are bending!" she cried.

So Mr. Preston ordered another engine for the tramline.
"Hi," said Rocket, the new engine. "I have metal stays in my
square firebox, and more metal in my frames. I won't bend
and bulge !"
"Is a bell like a whistle?" he chuckled.
"Mr. Preston!" called Isabel.

We'll strengthen your frames, and give you a square firebox," said Mr. Preston kindly to Isabel. "and Mr. Mcadam needs a lot of stone for his new roads that are covered with tar. Hmm, we must get you even more help."

Two steam lorries arrived with steel wheels. Clunkety clunk, they rattled over the rocky ground. Then one arrived, with solid rubber tyres, but it rattled along as well.

"Too much dust!" coughed Isabel.

It was time for some more railway engines.
"Hello, I'm here to help." chuffed Jack
"Me too." said Edith "Is a bell very loud?" she giggled.
And the work carried on.

One day, everyone was busy and
no one noticed three little boys with some copper coins.
"Faster!"shouted Joe the driver. "There's lots to do."
"Watch out!" cried Joe, as they went round a bend.

"Ooer!!" cried Isabel, as she toppled over!

"We're very sorry!" said the boys as they were told off.
"That was a very dangerous thing to do," said Joe.
"But it is a very bendy track."

Soon even more granite was needed for the new Tar Macadam roads. Isabel was fixed, a bigger hole was started and more engines arrived.

Derek, the crane, hauled up pans filled with stone, and he lowered Isabel and Edith down into the 'Sinking Hole'.

Each day, he shouted "lunch time!" or "blasting time!" and hauled them out again.

Now...far away from the quarry, a battle began. The quarrying carried on.

But soon the lorries were falling apart, so bigger steam engines, with bigger track, and ten ton steel wagons arrived. "We're here to do your job," they said, and the little engines were hoisted out to haul granite at the top.

"You're getting worn out," said Mr. Preston jnr.
"Time to change your firebox! A circular one
will do very nicely."

...and others arrived.

"Ow do," said Isabel and Edith

"Guten tag," said Klaus, Isabel's new driver.

"Bon Journo," said Antonio to Edith, as he started the fire.

The work went on.

When some men finally returned, there was lots to do.
So many new buildings were needed, that five humungous,
twelve ton lorries, with tyres filled with air, trundled down
a new road, into the Sinking Hole.
Derek, the engines, and the incline, had to go.

"No more work," said Isabel sadly, and all the steam
engines sat unwanted on the spoil bank.
The years slipped by as they slumbered ...until

One day, there was a a strange commotion.
Isabel was woken up by people from the Bagnall factory.
"We're saving you, for a new job," they said.
"Just me?" asked Isabel.
"You're the oldest, best one left," they said.
"Ooer, goodbye," she called to her friends, as she was loaded
onto the trailer.

Now, Isabel was polished and painted and placed on a plinth at Bagnall H.Q . and people came to see her.
"You know, there are 3000 engines just like me," she said proudly, "all over the world!"

But Bagnalls stopped building engines and yet again her job disappeared... and soon Isabel was the last bit of railway left.

"We'll have you dear," said the people from the town park.
"You are the oldest best engine
in Staffordshire."

"Hello, welcome. I'm a Bagnall steam engine." she said to
everyone, all through long cold winters and hot summers too.

But as she
sat there,
she
started
to feel...

...a bit wobbly,
and rusty,
and itchy,
and...nesh!

"Help!" she cried.
"My chimney
is sinking!"

"This is no good. We have to save Isabel!" said everyone that loved the little staffy engine.
"We'll build a railway especially for you."
So once again Isabel was cleaned up and fixed and painted.

Isabel went to her very own railway to pull carriages of people. "Thank you!" she said. "This time I'm home for good!"

Stoke
on Trent

Staffordshire

Stafford

Bagnalls

Amerton
Railway

Cannock

Lichfield

Tamworth

Isabel's
Journey